Ladybird Readers

Esio Trot

D0892881

9112000042 6619

Ladybird Books is part of the Penguin Random House group of companies
whose addresses can be found at global.penguinrandomhouse.com.
www.penguin.co.uk   www.puffin.co.uk   www.ladybird.co.uk

Penguin
Random House
UK

Text adapted from *Esio Trot*, first published by Puffin Books, 1990
This version published by Ladybird Books Ltd, 2020

ROALD
DAHL

Printed in China

A CIP catalogue record for this book is available from the British Library

ISBN: 978–0–241–36789–6

All correspondence to:
Ladybird Books
Penguin Random House Children's
80 Strand, London WC2R ORL

Ladybird 🐞 Readers

ROALD
DAHL

Esio Trot

Based on the original title
by Roald Dahl
Illustrated by Quentin Blake

Picture words

Mr. Hoppy

Mrs. Silver

Alfie the tortoise

alone

brave

backwards

lower

tool

ounces

weigh

Mr. Hoppy lived in a small flat near the top of a tall building. He lived alone, and only two things were very important to him.

The first thing was the flowers which grew on his balcony.

The second thing was Mrs. Silver.

Mrs. Silver was a very nice woman who lived below Mr. Hoppy's flat. They spoke every morning. Like Mr. Hoppy, she lived alone.

Every day, Mr. Hoppy thought, "I will invite her up for a cup of tea today," but he was never brave enough.

9

There was another problem, too.
Mrs. Silver had a small tortoise
called Alfie, and she gave all her
love to him.

Alfie lived in a little house on
Mrs. Silver's balcony, and when
Mr. Hoppy went outside, he could
see them together.

"I want to be that tortoise!"
he always thought.

One morning, Mr. Hoppy
called, "Good morning,
Mrs. Silver. How is Alfie today?"

"I'm worried about him, Mr. Hoppy,"
said Mrs. Silver. "I weighed him
when he first came to me 11 years
ago. He was 10 ounces then, and
he is only 13 ounces now. I want
him to grow."

Suddenly, Mr. Hoppy had an idea.

"Mrs. Silver," he said. "I think that
I can help. Wait there. I need to
write something for you."

Two minutes later, Mr. Hoppy came back on to his balcony with a piece of paper. He lowered it down to Mrs. Silver.

She read:

ESIO TROT, ESIO TROT,

WORG! WORG!

"What DOES it mean?" she asked.

"It's tortoise language," said
Mr. Hoppy. "Tortoises can only
understand backwards words.
It means:

'TORTOISE, TORTOISE,
GROW! GROW!'

Say these words to Alfie three times
a day, and he will get bigger."

Mrs. Silver did not look very sure,
but she said, "Mr. Hoppy, if this
helps, you will be my best friend
in the world!"

Back in his flat, Mr. Hoppy
thought of her words, and he did
a little dance.

For the next two days, Mr. Hoppy went to every pet shop in the city.

21

He bought more than a hundred
tortoises, and he brought them
home. They were all bigger
than Alfie.

Then, he made a clever tool.
He called it a tortoise-catcher.

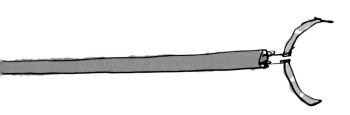

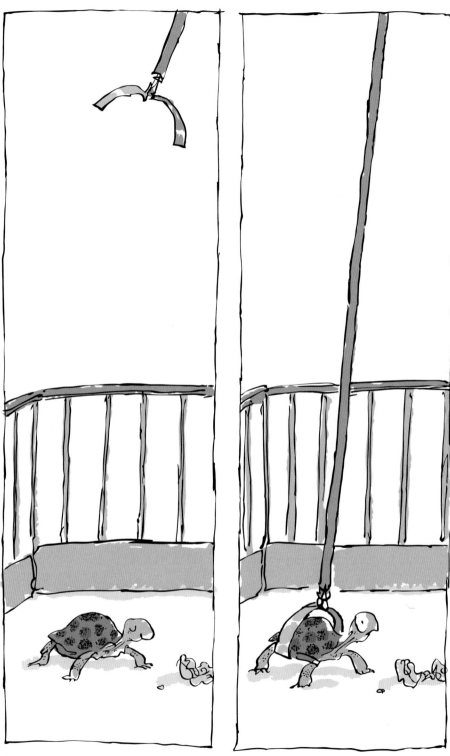

Mrs. Silver went out every afternoon at about two o'clock. One day, when she left, Mr. Hoppy went out on to his balcony with the tortoise-catcher.

He lowered his tool down on to Mrs. Silver's balcony, and he carefully pulled Alfie up.

Then, Mr. Hoppy went inside and weighed Alfie. Mrs. Silver was right: he was 13 ounces.

Now, Mr. Hoppy looked for a tortoise that weighed 15 ounces.

He found one that looked the same
as Alfie but was 2 ounces bigger.
"Wonderful!" he said.

He took it outside, and he lowered it carefully on to Mrs. Silver's balcony.

You see, Mr. Hoppy knew something important: children and animals grow slowly, so people do not see them grow.

Mrs. Silver came home, and she said to the tortoise,

"ESIO TROT, ESIO TROT,
WORG! WORG!"

"How is Alfie tonight, Mrs. Silver?"
Mr. Hoppy called.

"Oh, he is wonderful!"
said Mrs. Silver.

After that, Mr. Hoppy changed
Mrs. Silver's tortoise every week.

The next week,
he changed it
for a tortoise
that weighed
17 ounces.

Then, one
that weighed
19 ounces . . .

21 ounces . . .

23 ounces . . .

25 ounces . . .

and finally,
a 27-ounce
tortoise!

One evening, Mrs. Silver called up very excitedly, "Look, Mr. Hoppy! Alfie can't go into his house. He's too big!"

"Weigh him, Mrs. Silver," Mr. Hoppy called.

Mrs. Silver went and weighed him.
A minute later, she came back.

"27 ounces!" she shouted, excitedly.
"Oh, you big, wonderful boy, Alfie!
Clever Mr. Hoppy!"

Suddenly, Mr. Hoppy felt very brave. "Mrs. Silver," he said, "could I come down to your balcony and see Alfie?"

"Yes, of course!" said Mrs. Silver.

Mr. Hoppy hurried down. "He has grown big now," he said.

"You did it!" said Mrs. Silver. "Now, I must buy him a new house."

"Oh, THAT house is very pretty," said Mr. Hoppy. "Why don't you tell Alfie to get smaller?"

Then, he wrote on a piece of paper:

ESIO TROT, ESIO TROT,
TEG RELLAMS.

"Say these words to him now, Mrs. Silver," said Mr. Hoppy.

"I'll try that, then," said Mrs. Silver.
"If he gets smaller, you are the
cleverest man in the world!"

The next day, when Mrs. Silver
went out, Mr. Hoppy pulled the
tortoise up from her balcony with
his tortoise-catcher. Then, he found
a tortoise that was smaller but not
too small.

He lowered it down on to
Mrs. Silver's balcony.

41

That evening, Mr. Hoppy suddenly heard Mrs. Silver below. She was very excited.

"Mr. Hoppy! Alfie can go into his house now! Come and see!"

Mr. Hoppy ran down to
Mrs. Silver's flat.

She stood at the open door with a big
smile on her face. "You are the most
wonderful man in the world!" she
said. "Come and have a cup of tea."

They sat and had tea together.
Mrs. Silver smiled, and Mr. Hoppy
suddenly felt very brave.

"Mrs. Silver, please will you marry
me?" he said.

"Of course I will!" she said.
"Why didn't you ask me before?"

Activities

The key below describes the skills practiced in each activity.

Spelling and writing

Reading

Speaking

Critical thinking

Preparation for the Cambridge Young Learners exams

1 **Look and read. Choose the correct words and write them on the lines.** 📖 ✏️ ✿

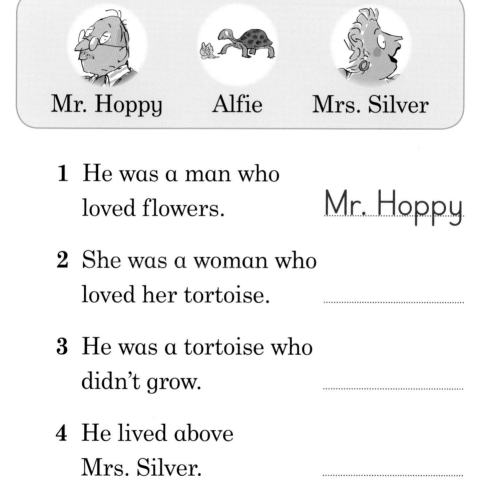

Mr. Hoppy   Alfie   Mrs. Silver

1 He was a man who loved flowers.   Mr. Hoppy

2 She was a woman who loved her tortoise.   ....

3 He was a tortoise who didn't grow.   ....

4 He lived above Mrs. Silver.   ....

2 Find the words.

ounces
alone
backwards
lower
tool
brave
weigh

frouncesibibravehestoolpojraloneiohweighbrdjlowerintbackwardstor

3 Write the missing letters.

a a b d e e g h l o r s s w

1 GROW WORG ←

b a ckwar d s

2

_____ o w _____ _____

3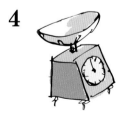

_____ l o n _____

4

_____ u n c _____ _____

5

_____ e i _____ _____

4 Circle the correct words.

Mr. Hoppy lived in a small flat near the top of a tall building. He lived alone, and only two things were very important to him.

The first thing was the flowers which grew on his balcony.

The second thing was Mrs. Silver.

6   7

1 Alfie the tortoise / **Mr. Hoppy** lived in a small flat near the top of a tall building.

2 He lived **alone, / backwards,** and only two things were very important to him.

3 The first thing was the flowers which grew on his **balcony. / tool.**

4 The second thing was **Mrs. Hoppy. / Mrs. Silver.**

5 **Read the text. Choose the correct words and write them next to 1—8.**

📖 ✏️ ⬡

was	could	gave	had
lived	thought	called	went

There ¹ ....._was_..... another problem, too.

Mrs. Silver ² .... a small tortoise

³ .... Alfie, and she ⁴ ....

all her love to him. He ⁵ .... in a

little house on Mrs. Silver's balcony, and

when Mr. Hoppy ⁶ .... outside,

he ⁷ .... see them together. "I want

to be that tortoise!" he always ⁸ ....

6 Ask and answer the questions with a friend. 🗨 ❓

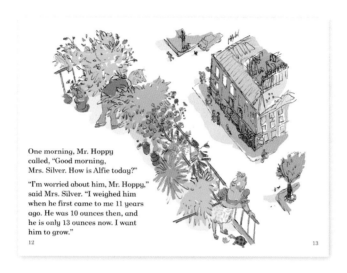

One morning, Mr. Hoppy called, "Good morning, Mrs. Silver. How is Alfie today?"

"I'm worried about him, Mr. Hoppy," said Mrs. Silver. "I weighed him when he first came to me 11 years ago. He was 10 ounces then, and he is only 13 ounces now. I want him to grow."

12   13

1 *Why is Mrs. Silver worried about Alfie?*

Because he isn't growing.

2 When did Mrs. Silver get Alfie?

3 How much did Alfie grow?

7 **Can you remember?**
Choose the correct words.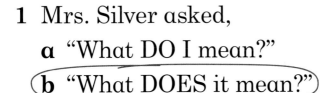

1 Mrs. Silver asked,
   a "What DO I mean?"
   b "What DOES it mean?"

2 Mr. Hoppy said,
   a "It's tortoise language."
   b "It isn't tortoise language."

3 Back in his flat, Mr. Hoppy
   a did a little dance.
   b did a big dance.

8 **Match the two parts of the sentences. Then, write them on the lines.** 📖 ✏️

1 Mr. Hoppy

2 He bought more than

3 Then, he made a clever tool

a a hundred tortoises.

b called a tortoise-catcher.

c went to every pet shop in the city.

1 Mr. Hoppy went to every pet shop in the city.

2 ....

....

3 ....

....

9 **Read the questions.**
Write complete answers.

1 What did Mrs. Silver do every afternoon at two o'clock?
   <u>Mrs. Silver went out every afternoon at two o'clock.</u>

2 What did Mr. Hoppy do one day when she left?

3 Where did he lower his tool?

4 What did he carefully do with it?

10 **Circle the correct sentences.**

1

a Mr. Hoppy looked for a tortoise that weighed 11 ounces.

b Mr. Hoppy looked for a tortoise that weighed 15 ounces.

2

a He found one that looked different from Alfie.

b He found one that looked the same as Alfie.

3

a Mrs. Silver was happy because Alfie was bigger.

b Mrs. Silver was sad because Alfie was bigger.

11 **Look and read. Write the correct words in the boxes.** 📖 ✏️ ❓

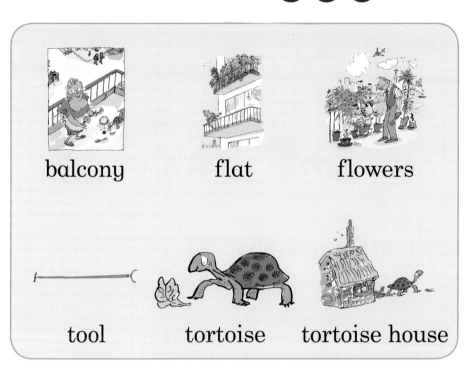

balcony

flat

flowers

tool

tortoise

tortoise house

Things Mr. Hoppy has	Things they both have	Things Mrs. Silver has
	balcony	

12 **Look and read. Write *true* or *false*.**

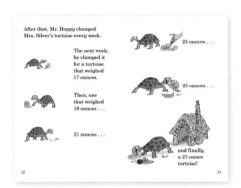

1 Mr. Hoppy changed
Mrs. Silver's tortoise
every week.   true

2 The tortoises got smaller
and smaller.   ....

3 One evening, the tortoise
couldn't go into his house.   ....

4 He weighed 57 ounces.   ....

5 Mrs. Silver was very happy.   ....

13 **Write the correct sentences.**

1 (brave) (felt) (Mr. Hoppy) (,)
(Suddenly) (very) (.)

Suddenly, Mr. Hoppy felt
very brave.

2 (Alfie) (and) (come) ("Could)
(down) (I) (see) (?")

....

....

3 (down) (hurried) (Mr. Hoppy) (.)

....

4 (big) ("He) (now) (.") (grown)
(has)

....

14 Read the text. Choose the correct words and write them next to 1—4. 📖 ✏️ ⬟

---

1 prettier   prettiest   very pretty

2 as small   smaller   smallest

3 wrote   has written   writes

4 Say   Said   Saying

"Oh, THAT house is ¹ <u>very pretty</u>," said Mr. Hoppy. "Why don't you tell Alfie to get ² _____?" Then, he

³ _____ on a piece of paper . . .

"⁴ _____ these words to him now, Mrs. Silver," said Mr. Hoppy.

15 Write *down*, *into*, or *up*.

The next day, when Mrs. Silver went out, Mr. Hoppy pulled the tortoise up from her balcony with his tortoise-catcher. Then, he found a tortoise that was smaller but not too small.

He lowered it down on to Mrs. Silver's balcony.

40

41

1 Mr. Hoppy pulled the tortoise ....up........................ from her balcony with his tortoise-catcher.

2 He lowered a smaller tortoise .... on to Mrs. Silver's balcony.

3 Mrs. Silver was very excited. "Mr. Hoppy! Alfie can go .... his house now!"

16 **Order the story. Write 1—5.** 📖

.... Mr. Hoppy asks Mrs. Silver to marry him.

......1...... Mrs. Silver wants Alfie to grow.

.... Mr. Hoppy lowers a smaller tortoise on to Mrs. Silver's balcony.

.... Mr. Hoppy lowers some bigger tortoises on to Mrs. Silver's balcony.

.... Mr. Hoppy buys lots of tortoises.

17 Talk to your friend about the story.
Use *First*, *Then*, *After that*, and
Finally.

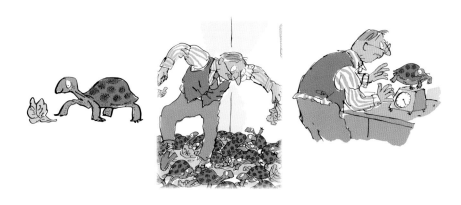

First, Mrs. Silver wanted
Alfie the tortoise to
grow bigger . . .

Ladybird Readers

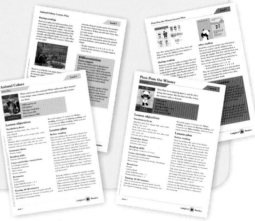